Driving the Invisible Bus

By Craig Bradley

Illustrations by Steve McCann

CABOODLE

A Catalogue record for this book is available from the
British Library.

ISBN-13: 978-0-9559711-8-1

Typeset in Century by Paul Wilson

Printed in the UK by CPI Cox & Wyman, Reading

The paper and board used in the paperback by Caboodle
Books Ltd are natural recyclable products made from wood
grown in sustainable forests. The manufacturing processes
conform to the environmental regulations of the country of
origin.

Caboodle Books Ltd
Riversdale, 8 Rivock Avenue, Steeton, BD20 6SA
Tel: 01535 656015

Contents

Remote Control

I loved it on my holidays
I had a great time then
if I had a remote control
I'd rewind those days again.

When the maths lesson drags on
and on and on and on and on
I'd zap it on fast forward
until the bell has gone.

Then when everyone is happy
I'd be really, really clever
and I'd press it on to pause
to make the moment last forever.

Driving The Invisible Bus
(for Dancing Dads everywhere)

Dads dancing, dancing Dads
Dads dancing, dancing Dads
Look like men, act like lads
Dads dancing, dancing Dads

Drive the invisible bus
Drive the invisible bus
Everyone will stare at us
Drive the invisible bus

Do the box stacker
Do the box stacker
Jumping like a fire cracker
Do the box stacker

Do the window cleaning
Do the window cleaning
Oh you should have seen him
Do the window cleaning

Do the downhill ski-ing
Do the downhill ski-ing
Can't believe what I am seeing
Do the downhill ski-ing

Do the slow motion
Do the slow motion
Let's cause a slow commotion
Do the slow motion

Do the dying for the loo
Do the dying for the loo
His face is going blue
Do the dying for the loo

Mrs Burton's Curtains

Mrs Burton's curtains
are never open wide
so no one ever really knows
what's going on inside

Maybe it's a witches cave
with cobwebs on the wall
and she mixes magic potions
in a cauldron down the hall

Maybe she's caught an alien
someone like ET
and she keeps the curtains tightly closed
so no one else can see

It could be a secret casino
where people take a chance
or some kind of crazy nightclub
where people go to dance

It could be a deep dark dungeon
beyond your wildest dreams
full of ghostly shadows
and a thousand scary screams

Mrs Burton's curtains
are never open wide
maybe we will never know
the secrets that they hide

Biscuit Bingo

Eyes down for a full house
come and learn the lingo
so take a seat
and have a treat
with a game of biscuit bingo

You and me
   Rich Tea
I'll have a bit of that
   KitKat
Just the job
   Hobnob
Jolly Roger
   Jammie Dodger
Born to win
   Penguin
In your dreams
   Custard Creams
Jump in the lake
   Jaffa Cake

Athlete's foot
        Gingernut
Make my day
        Breakaway
They're my bestives
        Digestives

Football Bingo

Yellow card
    Frank Lampard
From Paris to Peckham
    David Beckham
Rock n' Roll
    Joe Cole
Hear the wind blowing
    Michael Owen

Jolly good fellow
    Fabio Capello
Three little pigs
    Ryan Giggs
George Clooney
    Wayne Rooney
Never give up
    FA Cup

Midnight creeper
Goalkeeper
Take your pick
Hat trick
Cup of tea
Referee
Aunty Elsie
Chelsea

I'm delighted
Man United
What a pity
Man City
April Fool
Liverpool
Strawberry jam
West Ham

The Shape Of A Football

I remember when my imagination escaped
and all my world became football shaped...

Football boots, football laces
football people, football faces.

Football houses, football cars
football moon, football stars.

Football clouds, football seas
football birds, football bees.

Football Dads, football Mums
football fingers, football thumbs.

Football dinner, football tea
football you, football me.

My imagination had no limits at all
when all my world was a big football.

My Hometown Team

You have to support your hometown team
even when they're three-nil down
so I support my hometown team
and they're called Halifax Town.

If Town are playing at home
I'll go and watch them play
and get off at the bus stop
by the ground they call the Shay.

It's not a really fancy ground
like those on *Match of the Day*
I suppose it looks a bit worn out
but hey, I like it that way.

There's a man with a caravan
that he parks in the parking bay
and you can buy some pie and peas
in a little plastic tray.

We'll never win the FA Cup,
that is just a dream
but I'll always shout for Halifax
cos they're my hometown team.

Dream Goal

Last night in my dreams
I scored the perfect goal
I knew when I got the ball
that I was on a roll.

I ghosted past one defender
like he was standing still
I started doing tricks
like I was playing for Brazil.

I just kept right on going
heart thumping in my chest
I knew I was unstoppable,
I knew I was the best.

I got to the penalty area
and had a little glance
then fired in a screamer
the goalie didn't stand a chance.

The crowd went ballistic
cos we had won the cup
I was living in a dream world
and then I just woke up.

Raindrops

When it rains I stand outside
    until the weather clears,
I like to watch the raindrops
    turn cobwebs to chandeliers.

I'll stand outside forever
    until the weather's fine,
watching raindrops hang like pearls
    from the washing line.

Lost Hat

I've lost my hat
or has my hat lost me?

I was playing football
so I took it off you see.

It kept on blowing off
and it got stuck up a tree

so I left it in the park
when I came in for my tea

and now I've lost my hat
or has my hat lost me?

Poetry Pitstop

this   poem
         is
                                              all
                                      over
      the   place

This poem needs a M.O.T.
a complete overhaul
the repetition, repetition, repetition
repetition just doesn't work at all.

Your battery needs a re-charge
I'll get the jump leads from the van
it'll never be a classic
but I'll do the best I can.

The rhymes have gone all rusty
and the line endings all

                                        wrong
but little drop of oil
will make it flow just like a song.

And what about the rhythm eh?
What about the beat?
A poem won't start without a heart,
it's completely incomplete.

This poem has lost its sparkle
I'll get some spark plugs from the shop
and a brand new set of brake pads
so it knows when to STOP.

My Pet Snowman

Never had a dog, never had a cat
but I had a pet snowman, how about that!

Made him big, made him strong
made him to last all winter long

Pebble eyes, carrot nose
icy fingers, icy toes

We'd play games, sit and chat
he let me wear his snowman's hat

We'd laugh and sing and stay up late
My pet snowman, my best mate

He disappeared one sunny day
but thoughts of him won't melt away

Come next winter I'll say hello
to my favourite pet who's made of snow

Grow Your Own Alien

Grow your own alien
they're not that bad
grow an alien mum or an alien dad

Once you've grown one
then you can grow another
maybe an alien sister or an alien brother

It's easy to do
just add water
to grow yourself an alien daughter

With alien fingers
and an alien face
zooming about all over the place

Making noises
you can't ignore
making smells you haven't smelt before

If you've never seen
an alien creature
just have a good look at your teacher!!

Mrs Macaroon

Mrs Macaroon
Mrs Macaroon
Sleeps in the staff room every afternoon

Mrs Macaroon
Mrs Macaroon
Face like a turnip and nose like a prune

Mrs Macaroon
Mrs Macaroon
Went for a holiday on the moon

Mrs Macaroon
Mrs Macaroon
Said that she went for a week last June

Mrs Macaroon
Mrs Macaroon
Flew up there in a big balloon

Mrs Macaroon
Mrs Macaroon
Took a packed lunch and her pet racoon

Mrs Macaroon
Mrs Macaroon
Saw a shooting star fly past Neptune

Mrs Macaroon
Mrs Macaroon
She really wants to go back soon

My Greatest Hit

I've never had a greatest hit
but this just might be it
maybe the words you're reading now
will be my greatest hit.

I don't want a lot of money
well, maybe just a bit
but all the money in the world
couldn't buy my greatest hit.

It might be poem about daffodils
or a big banana split
you'll see me on the telly
talking about my greatest hit.

I'd have a personal trainer
I'll look super lean and fit
all the world will know the words
to my greatest hit.

So I'll keep on trying
cos I'm never gonna quit
maybe the words you're reading now
will be my greatest hit.

On The Bus

There's a goth girl behind you
just over there
with a flour white face
and coal black hair.

There's a nice old lady
who looks like your Gran
she's laughing and chatting
to a wrinkly old man.

There's a woman with a kid
and a toddler in a pram
who's eating a doughnut
and covered in jam.

There's a teenager
in a Man U shirt
sat next to a girl
in a really short skirt.

There's a chav in sunglasses
that she's wearing for the pose
and a grubby schoolkid
who keeps picking his nose.

And then there's me
not making a fuss
just calmly checking out
the other people on the bus.

Little Girl Dancing At A Wedding

To be really, really happy
you don't have to do your head in
just pretend that you're a little girl
dancing at a wedding.

Put your arms out, your head back
and spin round and round
soon you'll be floating
six inches off the ground.

You'll forget all your troubles
like that maths exam you're dreading
you'll be happy as a lamb
when its winter coat is shedding
you'll be glowing like that bowl of soup
you like to dip your bread in
when you pretend you're just a little girl

dancing at a wedding.

Disco Dad

Dad's disco dancing is dire
I know that he's a tryer
but it's no joke
he looks like a bloke
with his underpants on fire.

When Mum Married A Martian

When Mum married a Martian
I didn't know what to say
because Mum marrying a Martian
isn't something she does everyday.

She got her best bag and suitcase
and packed all her things away,
she smiled at me and I smiled at her
and I knew she'd be OK,

then she buzzed off on her honeymoon
around the Milky Way.

No One Else Is You

Everyone's a one off
no one does the stuff you do
no one smiles the way you smile
cos no one else is you.

Everyone is different
it doesn't matter who
no one thinks the way you think
cos no one else is you.

No one laughs or walks
or talks or sings or does the things you do
everyone's a one off
cos no one else is you.

Big Shop

When Mum does the big shop
she likes to have it planned
she knows her way round Tesco's
like the back of her hand.

Mum snaps up all the bargains
before they have all gone
and whizzes round the aisles
like Formula One.

Sometimes she buys things
just for the sake
like some yukky low fat custard
and a rock hard birthday cake.

She buys bunches of old bananas
that are past their sell-by day
and when we get home she makes
us eat them straight away.

I can tell when Mum's finished
cos the trolley's jampacked
my Mum's really good at shopping
she's the best and that's a fact.

What Mum Likes

Mum likes spiders
but doesn't like flies
she likes hellos
but not goodbyes.

She doesn't like slugs
and she doesn't like snails
but she likes dolphins,
seals and whales.

She likes catching the bus
but she doesn't like waiting
she likes chewing her tongue
when she's concentrating.

She likes going to Ibiza
so she can have a rest
she likes playing with her hair
when she gets a bit stressed.

She likes David Beckham
and Coronation Street
she likes the smell of bacon
but she doesn't eat meat.

She likes Cadbury's Flakes
and lager and lime
and I think she likes Dad
most of the time.

She likes singing along with Abba
and watching Trisha on TV
but best of all
my Mum likes me.

Just Like Eastenders
(Duffduffduffdumdumdoodleoodle)

It's just like Eastenders
in our house,
but what can you do
when you find out that your Mum
is really your Aunty Sue?

Duffduffduffdumdumdoodleoodle

It's just like Eastenders
in our house
so tell me what's the score
when you find out that your brother
isn't your brother anymore?

Duffduffduffdumdumdoodleoodle

It's just like Eastenders
in our house
I'm telling you it's a mess
when I came home from school
and saw my Dad wearing a dress.

Duffduffduffdumdumdoodleoodle

It's just like Eastenders
in our house
It's messing with my head
so I think that I'll turn over
and watch Coronation Street instead.

Duffduffduffdumdumdoodleoodle

Billy The Kid

Billy's got this big hat
that his Mum got cheap
from the Oxfam shop
up the high street.

It's too big or summat,
must be the wrong size,
cos it keeps slipping down
over his eyes.

When he wears it, he smiles,
reckons he looks
like that bloke on the telly
who wrestles crocodiles.

One windy day it blew
off and flew up the road.
Everyone laughed
except Billy, he just stood

there he did, looking silly.
He wasn't a crocodile
wrestler at all, just a kid,
just like me, just Billy.

Wallpaper Faces

When the day turns into night
and the sun and moon swap places
my bedroom wall comes alive
with weird wallpaper faces.

One looks like a dragon
one looks like a bear
one looks like Homer Simpson
with custard coloured hair.

One looks like a monster
that I once saw on TV
one has got a cheeky face
and looks a bit like me.

One looks like an evil clown
one looks like a fairy
one looks like my maths teacher
but that's a bit too scary.

If I get too frightened
when these faces all appear
then I just flick my light on
and these faces disappear.

Sucking Soup Through A Straw

Sucking soup
through a straw
makes your mouth sore
and your face
go purple like a prune.

You'll spill it
and slurp
and dribble
and burp,
that's why
they invented the spoon.

The Australian Alien

It looks like a wombat
or something on Dr Who.
It's got ears like a koala bear
and a tail like a kangaroo.

It's only as big as a wallaby
but it has a roar like thunder.
It's my little Australian Alien
who lives in the land down under.

Getting Up Early

When you get up early
the world belongs to you
the grass beneath looks
greener than green,
the sky above brand new.

All the birds are singing,
the air is applesweet,
the world is one big fruit bowl
that looks good enough to eat.

The trees sound like they're whispering
as they rustle in the breeze
they're saying every day's a doorway
and you have got the keys.

Wordsurfing

You have to get up earlier
  than you've ever done before
    and listen to the wordwaves
      as they gently lap the shore.

You start to feel the rhythm
  you feel the ebb and flo
    when you catch the perfect word
      that's when you have to go.

So jump up on your wordboard
  soon you'll soar just like a bird
    and that is when your surfing
      on the crest of a word.

PiePod

Forget the iPod
that's yesterday's news
what about a Piepod
for any pie you choose?

To keep a PiePod in your pocket
would be a good idea
you could press a little button
and a pie would just appear

It wouldn't matter where you are
from Sheffield to Sydney
you could have a cheese and onion pie
or maybe a nice steak and kidney

Then you'd press another button
for your ketchup or your mustard
and finish off with an apple pie
but don't forget the custard

Mr Hughes' Electric Shoes

Mr Hughes is an inventor
who invents all kinds of things
he once built a flying hoover
that hovered on hoover wings

It whizzed and flew around the room
until it blew a fuse
then Mr Hughes thought he'd invent
a pair of electric shoes

These shoes are air-conditioned
with a fan inside a box
so in the summer your feet won't smell
no more smelly socks

They're handy if you work outside
like a builder or a postie
cos when it's cold you plug them in
to keep your toes all toasty

And if you play football
flick the auto-pilot switch
and you'll run rings round anybody
on any football pitch

Inventing stuff is really cool
there's a million things you can do
when I'm a Mister like Mr Hughes
I'll be an inventor too

Have You Heard The Moon?

Have you heard the moon?
Have you heard it sigh
as it sits collecting stardust
on its moonshelf in the sky?

Have you heard the sun?
Have you heard it sing
and shine the air with promises
of what the day may bring?

Have you heard the rain?
Have you heard it cry
sobbing its broken heart out
when its tears fill the sky?

Have you heard the wind?
Have you heard it moan?
Its wicked wind chill factor
will chill you to the bone

Have you heard the sea?
Have you heard it roar
as it rolls and swells and slowly
waves goodbye towards the shore?

The Best Presents I've Never Had

- My shadow in a box
- invisible socks
- 1 time machine
- 1 elf
- a gazillion quid
- a dragon called Sid
- a room that cleans itself

- 1 faraway star caught in a jar
- a bowl of tap dancing fishes
- 1 single moonbeam
- my best ever dream
- a genie with three magic wishes

- a castle in the sky
- the ability to fly
- teeth that never go bad
- 1 white horse with wings

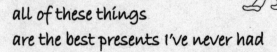

all of these things
are the best presents I've never had

Full. Stops.

Sometimes. Full. Stops.
Just. Get. In. The. Way.
And. Interrupt. What.
You. Want. To. Say.

Too. Many. Full. Stops.
Makes. Me. Want. To. Shout.
So. The. Next. Time.
You. Want. To. Use. One.

Leave it out

This Is The Classroom

Chair, desk, paper, pen,
all the numbers one to ten
cricket bat, tennis ball,
alphabet stuck on the wall
pencil sharpener, whiteboard too,
pots of paint, red, white and blue,
big TV and radio
This is the classroom where I go

Teacher's cup for her tea,
water bottle just for me,
model boat, doll's house,
Ant the fish, Dec the mouse,
science corner, weighing scales,
books on history, books on whales,
three computers in a row
This is the classroom where I go

Guitar cases, homework books,
PE bags left on hooks,
class photo in a frame,
Scrabble if you want a game,
Jack, Ben, Keisha and Matt,
Bilal, Megan, Nathan Platt
all the best friends that I know
This is the classroom where I go

The Impossible Sausages

We're the impossible sausages
no one can resist
we're always Number 1
on your shopping list

We're the impossible sausages
we are pretty flash
a sizzle for your sandwich
a banger for your mash

It's impossible not to like us
we'll make you lick your lips
we're brilliant with beans
we're chiptastic with chips

We're the impossible sausages
a toad for the hole
we're the ones for you
we are sausage rock n' roll

We're the impossible sausages
the nation's favourite tea
so cook me up a storm
and make a meal of me

Punctuation Party

Exclamation mark
was a bit of a lark
cos all he did was shout
!!

Question mark
just sat in the dark
and no one could him figure out
?????????????????????????????

    The paragraphs
    were a load of laughs
    in their sparkly party jackets

(Pass-The-Parcel was a sentence
wrapped up in a pair of brackets)

CAPITAL LETTERS
DANCED ALL NIGHT
TILL SHE WAS READY TO DROP

Then the punctuation party was over
and came to a full stop
....

If You Were A Fruit Which Fruit Would You Be?

If you were a fruit
which fruit would you be?
Would you be an apple
living on an appletree?

Would you be a big banana
a snack for an ape?
Would you be a grapefruit?
Would you be a grape?

Would you be a happy mango
carefree and jolly
or sad eyed melon
feeling quite melon colly?

Would you be a strawberry
for a milkshake?
Would you like to be
a little cherry on a cake?

I'd like to be a coconut
the biggest on the tree
but if you were a fruit
which fruit would you be?

Word Party

The dictionary had a party
the words all came along
I want to tell you what happened
don't worry it won't take too long

DISCO was first on the dance floor
GIGGLE came for the laugh
BONGO got into the rhythm
BUBBLE stayed in for a bath
CRISP came in a packet
PEANUT came out of his shell
GOSSIP told all the stories
SECRET didn't tell
HUNGRY ate all the sarnies
GREEDY had more than his share
SPONGE was washing his car
SHAMPOO was washing her hair
SNEAKY got in without paying
PATIENCE stood in the queue
SERIOUS stood without smiling

SMELLY just stood by the loo
THIRSTY started drinking
SNIFFLE started to sneeze
NAUGHTY started a foodfight
PIZZA got covered in cheese
FRIENDLY was laughing and waving
DIAMOND shone like a jewel
MUSIC played the trumpet
JOKER played the fool

The word party lasted a long time
it went on till quarter to three
when it finally finished
the last word to leave was ME

What Does The Rain Think It's Doing?

What does the rain
        think it's doing?
It's messing with my head
it's pouring and pouring and pouring
oh I wish it was sunny instead

What does the sun
        think it's doing?
It's making my nose go all red
it's shining and shining and shining
oh I wish it was windy instead

What does the wind
        think it's doing?
I should have stayed in bed
it's blowing and blowing and blowing
oh I wish it was snowing instead

What does the snow
        think it's doing?
It's covered the old garden shed
it's falling and falling and falling
oh I wish it was foggy instead

What does the fog
        think it's doing?
The sight of it fills me with dread
it's misty and misty and misty
oh I wish it was raining instead

*What does the rain
        think it's doing???*

Love Poem For The Girl Wearing Glasses I Saw In McDonald's

Tell me now
if I'm able
to park myself
at your table

Tell me now
give me a clue
can I sit down
next to you?

I like your hair,
your smile, your eyes
I like the way
you dip your fries

If love is a lock
you hold the keys
my heart feels
like melted cheese

I have never
felt so sweet
you make my heart
McSkip a beat.

My Happy Meal
I'll give to you
come share my burger
made for two

Walking Down The High Street

High Street, my street
walking down the high street
high street, my street
walking down the street

Specsavers, shoes from Clarks
Argos, Woolies, Marks and Sparks
Nettos, Topshop, JJB's
Greggs, Farmfoods, KFC's
Mothercare, buy a big pram
Carphone Warehouse and Oxfam
WHSmith, B&Q
Sainbury's, Tesco's
Morrisons too

High Street, my street
walking down the high street
high street, my street
walking down the street

Dorothy Perkins, HMV
Blockbusters for a DVD
Poundland, Primark and New Look
Waterstones for a cookery book
BHS, buy a new vest
Boots, Asda and Nat West
McDonalds and Subways
Thomas Cook for my holidays

High street, my street
walking down the high street
high street, my street
walking down the street

Funfair

The world is a great big funfair

all the rides are free

so slide the slide

enjoy the ride

and don't forget to wheeeeeee!!!!

Smallest Leaf, Tallest Tree

I'm the smallest leaf
>on the tallest tree

I'm the strongest sugar
>in the weakest tea

I'm the laziest buzz
>from the busiest bee

I'm the baldest head
>on the hairiest flea

I'm the wildest wave
>on the calmest sea

I'm the littlest lock
>with the biggest key

I'm the smoothest skin
>on the knobbliest knee

I'm the smallest leaf
>on the tallest tree

Let's Not And Say That We Did

Let's pretend to be spacemen
moonwalking on the moon
Let's do it once then do it again
every afternoon
Let's imagine we live in a spaceship
that looks like a giant pan lid
    Let's have a go
    Let's UFO
    Let's not and say that we did

Let's pretend to be sailors
lost on a stormy sea
A pair of shipwrecked survivors
who won't be home for tea
Let's imagine we're Captain Nemo
wrestling a giant squid
    Let's do something frantic
    Let's sail the Atlantic
    Let's not and say that we did

Let's pretend to be cowboys
riding through the west
You be the bad guy, I'll be the good
a sheriff's star pinned to my vest
Let's be on the trail of an outlaw
just like Billy the Kid

Let's ride out today
Let's yippee hi ay
Let's not and say that we did

C'mon
Let's put on a show
Let's have a go
Let's not and say
that we did

Don't Be A Cauliflower

Don't be a cauliflower
when you can be a rose
Don't be a dripping tap
when you can be a hose
Don't be a nostril
when you can be a nose

You can be anything
you have got the power
but please, please, please
don't be a cauliflower

Don't be a crumb
when you can be a cake
Don't be a puddle
when you can be a lake
Don't be the milk
when you can be a shake

You can be anything
you have got the power
but please, please, please
don't be a cauliflower

Don't be a tennis ball
when you can be a racket
Don't be a jumper
when you can be a jacket
Don't be a Hobnob
when you can be the packet

You can be anything
you have got the power
but please, please, please
don't be a cauliflower

Secrets With Socks On

Some feet know where they're going
some just go with the flow
some feet walk really quickly
while others just walk really slow

Some feet are skinny and hairy
some are bald and fat
some feet jump into puddles
while others don't bother with that

Some feet have shiny shoes on
some wear trainers and pumps
some feet have corns and verrucas
while others are covered in bumps

Some feet are made for dancing
some for kicking a ball
some are really ticklish
while others aren't ticklish at all

Some feet go sweaty and cheesy
some remain hidden from view
feet are just secrets with socks on
and they're keeping their secrets from you

Grandad In Space

Grandad is always thinking
his head is all over the place
one day he sat down and told me
he wanted to fly into space
He told me he went down the market
and showed me the stuff that he'd bought
you need the proper equipment
to be an astronaut

First he built a rocket
out of some old bits and bobs
then he had a cup of tea
and half a dozen Hobnobs
He painted the rocket silver
with paint that he got from his shed
then he was ready for blast off
but he had some more Hobnobs instead

He made some anti-gravity slippers
from some tinfoil and string
and a big Buzz Lightyear space-belt
out of an old rubber ring
He made an alien-proof cardie
with earmuffs, scarf and flatcap
then, when everything was ready
he looked at the moon on a map

He said 'Now that's where I'm going,
I'll set off at quarter to three
and if it doesn't start raining
I'll get back in time for my tea'
Then he started hurtling
towards the nearest star
when he got there, he had a kip
and put his false teeth in a jar

He whizzed around the planets
at the amazing speed of light
then ate an emergency Hobnob
to soothe his appetite
He went to the moon for a nosey
for a quick look around
he wrote **GRANDAD WAS HERE** in big letters
upon the dusty ground

Then when it was home time
he opened the escape hatch
and made a cool crash landing
slapbang in his old cabbage patch
When Grandad told me this story
he had a big smile on his face
I'm really proud of my Grandad
the first ever Grandad in space

Trees

In the summer
trees are brilliant
they look really smart
their leaves are shiny green
just like a work of art
but in winter trees
are leafless
and
they
hold
a
differ
ent
pose
Trees look a bit embarrassed without
their summer clothes

When I Took My Tractor On X-Factor

When I took my tractor
on X-Factor
this is what they said
'You have to sing
or do something'
so I bought a farm instead

Hilda The Builder

Hilda was a builder
who lived down the town

she built her own house
but the wind blew it down

and everybody wore a frown
cos Hilda the builder it kilda

Shotput Sam And His Sporting Gang

Shotput Sam
there he goes
dropped a shotput on his toes

Long jump Jane
she's unique
jumped herself into next week

Javelin Jim
with javelin spear
used it once to pierce his ear

Discus Dave
one of my mates
practises with dinner plates

High Jump Gemma
see her fly
lost her knickers in the sky

Superglue

I bumped

into Bianca

in B&Q

I was buying

a tube

of superglue

I said Bianca, Bianca

I'm stuck on you

The Sky Is Not The Limit

The sky is not the limit
cos above it are the stars
and above those are the planets
like Jupiter and Mars

The sky is not the limit
there's a universe out there
with galaxies and milky ways
for all of us to share

So I have this thing to tell you
that will make you feel like grinning
something to astound you
and make your head start spinning

The sky is not the limit
it is only the beginning

Girl With A Lollipop

Girl with a lollipop
who will you grow up to be?
Will you be the Prime Minister
looking serious on TV?

Will you be a mechanic
and fix a carburettor?
Or maybe you'll be a doctor
and make sick people better?

Will you be a popstar
with a milliontrillion fans?
Or perhaps a brave explorer
of strange exotic lands?

You could be a comedian
making us all laugh?
You could be a plumber
and come and fix my bath?

You might work in Sainsbury's
or maybe the local shop?
Who will you grow up to be
girl with a lollipop?

Forever

If you can see a forest
in a falling autumn leaf
or a desert in a single
grain of sand
if you can see the ocean
in one drop of summer rain
then you can hold forever in your hand

If you can see the goodness
in everybody's soul
then you will see a diamond
in a dusty piece of coal

If you can hear the laughter
of a flashing midnight star
if you can be happy
just being who you are
then you will hold forever in your hand

Whatever You Want It To Be Day

Eat A Bun Day
Have Some Fun Day
Walk Really Slow Day
Call Everyone Joe Day

Lay On The Floor Day
Learning To Snore Day
Bark Like A Dog Day
Lost In The Fog Day

Crazy Hair Day
Scary Stare Day
Dance Like Your Dad Day
Look Really Mad Day

Walk Like A Chicken Day
Nose Picking Day
Go For A Swim Day
Sing A Hymn Day

Wave At A Teacher Day
Invent A Strange Creature Day
Blow Your Own Trumpet Day
Butter A Crumpet Day

This and That Day
Wear A Silly Hat Day
Be A T-Rex Day
Whatever Next Day

Eat A Dippy Egg Day
Hop On One Leg Day
Ride A Bobsleigh Day
Call It A Day Day

A Box of Moments

Under my bed
there is a box
covered in glitter
that twinkles like a star
it's an important box
full of my favourite moments

Inside is the time
I got my first bike
and the time we had a picnic
on the beach
I remember the sand
in the sandwiches,
the sea, the sun
and the melted KitKats
that was a good moment
one to treasure

Sometimes
I open the box, take one out
and share a moment with myself
If you want I'll share a moment with you

This one

Igloos

When

an Eskimo

wants to build a house

to keep out of the weather

he simply makes   some bricks

from snow and igloos   them all together

Bubble

Once I was sat on our front step
just looking up our street
when out of the blue
a bubble flew
and landed at my feet

I don't know where it came from
I don't have a clue
it just shimmered
and glittered and glimmered
cos that's what bubbles do

Then, suddenly, it flew on the breeze
so high I could hardly see
I often think
about that bubble
I wonder if it thinks about me

Tarzan In Tesco's

I saw Tarzan in Tesco's

he was buying some fruit and veg

I know a secret about Tarzan

his real name is Reg

Mum Works On The Photocopier

Mum works on the photocopier
    on the second floor
she does a load of copying
    then does a load more
she copies all sorts of things
    I've never seen before
I can see her sometimes
    through the window in the door

Mum works on the photocopier
    works from 10 till 2
sometimes she comes and sits in class
    if there's not a lot to do
but when she's really busy
    you have to join a queue
I'd really like to help her
    but I haven't got a clue

Mum works on the photocopier
    copies this and that
I see her laughing with the teachers
    when they pop round for a chat
Mum makes you feel like smiling
    even when you're feeling flat
I want to be just like her
    think I'll be a copycat

Mum works on the photocopier
    to her it's not a chore
she loves it when she puts her ink
    and paper in a drawer
but she doesn't like the papercuts
    that make her fingers sore
Mum works on the photocopier
    on the second floor

Spooky Dog

Spooky dog
Spooky dog
Everybody do the dog

My best mate lives up our street
at number twenty-nine
he has got this spooky dog
I'm glad that it's not mine
cos everytime I see him
I get shivers down my spine

At night he creeps in shadows
down by the railway line
and there he howls just like a wolf
beneath the pale moonshine
all night I hear the echoes
of his bloodcurdling whine

There's something strange about this dog
something I can't define
he appears out of nowhere
like some kind of ghostly sign
I'm really, really, really, really glad
that it's not mine

Spooky dog
Spooky dog
Everybody do the dog

The Total Eclipse Of Uncle Dave

Uncle Dave's face
    was as big as the moon
when he popped round
    last Monday afternoon

I had to rub my eyes
    couldn't believe what I could see
when I saw the moon
    in our kitchen drinking tea

I remember one night
    playing football in the park
when Uncle Dave's face
    started growing dark

He made some gurgling noises
    he began to rant and rave
it was the total eclipse
    of Uncle Dave

Dreaming In Colour

A smokysleepy shower of blue,
a glittering glare of green,
a yawn of yellow, purple too
with orange tucked between

A beautiful, burning blush of pink,
a shock of silver so cold,
a riot of red with a tiny hint
of peach beneath the gold

Bob's Gone Bonkers

Bob's gone bonkers
totally loopyloo
his eyes have gone all bulgy
his ears have gone all blue

Bob's gone bonkers
he's shaking his fist
ranting and raving
got his knickers in a twist

Bob's gone bonkers
really doolally
he's drooling like a mad old dog
and barking up the alley

Bob's gone bonkers
it's not very funny
he's really going off on one
he's not a happy bunny

Bob's gone bonkers
he has lost the plot
all his face is burning
his cheeks are really hot

Bob's gone bonkers
there isn't any doubt
we better call the fire brigade
to come and put him out

Could Have Been Worse

Dad could have been a boxer
the heavyweight world champ
Dad could have been a down and out
living like a tramp

Mum could have been a popstar
like Christina Aguilera
Mum could have been a chav
a crazy bling bling wearer

Could have been better
Could have been worse
Dad's a taxi driver
Mum's a nurse

Dad could have been a hero
many wars he fought
Dad could have been a woman
that's not a pretty thought

Mum could have been an actress
always on TV
Mum could have been a man
but where would that leave me?

There's no one like my Mum and Dad
in the entire universe
I suppose it could have been better
but I know it could have been worse

Dad's a taxi driver
Mum's a nurse

Hey Mister Scarecrow

Hey Mister Scarecrow
what do you know
all alone in your field all day?

I've seen you before
with your arms of straw
and your head all stuffed full of hay

Do you dream
your scarecrow dreams
when the moon comes out to play?

Or, when no one sees
do you dance with the trees
and waltz the world away?

Hey Mister Scarecrow
what do you know
all alone in your field all day?

Does your heart beat?
Have you got smelly feet?
When you get older will your straw turn grey?

What goes through your mind?
Are you funny, sweet and kind
or is there something you don't want to say?

Can your eyes see?
If you wave at me
are you frightened that I'll run away?

Hey Mister Scarecrow
what do you know
all alone in your field all day?

I Know You Got Soul

It's the way you dust the crumbs
when you scoff a sausage roll

It's the way you spill the milk
when you fill your cornflake bowl

It's the way you lace your trainers
when you go for a stroll

That's how I know you got soul

It's the way you never blow your top
and keep your self-control

It's the way you slice your onions
when you make a casserole

It's the way you keep your chin up
when you score a daft own goal

That's how I know you got soul

It's the way you never run and hide
in your cubbyhole

It's the way you play your football
and look just like Joe Cole

It's the way you keep on going
though every single rigmarole

That's how I know you got soul

Crazy Hair

I saw this bloke with crazy hair
up and down and everywhere

This bloke's hair was overgrown
this bloke's hair had a mind of its own

This bloke's hair stood out a mile
this bloke's hair had no style

It was a crow's nest on his head
I think he'd just got out of bed

It was something the cat dragged in
something you'd find in a wheelie bin

If they had a prize he'd win the cup
his hair was a hairball the cat coughed up

But he's not bothered, he doesn't care
he's just a bloke with crazy hair

Last

Last bottle in the crate
Last pea on the plate
Last star in the sky
Last tear in your eye

Last crisp in the packet
Last trouser, shirt and jacket
Last loaf in the shop
Last bucket, last mop

Last match in the box
Last pair of sweaty socks
Last smile that you smiled
Last lion in the wild

Last wish that came true
Last time you got the flu
Last dream that you had
Last apple gone bad

Last grin that you grinned
Last whisper on the wind
Last chance that you took
Last poem in this book

Craig Bradley is a professional poet, writer and performer who tours the UK sharing his passion and infectious enthusiasm for words.

He performs in schools, libraries, museums, art galleries, hospitals and literary festivals.

He has held many writing residencies in libraries, schools, prisons, youth offending teams, hospitals and literary festivals. In 2003 he was Calderdale Libraries first ever Reader In Residence, and has read his work on radio and TV.

Amongst other things, Craig has been a stand-up comedian, roadie, heavy metal drummer, window cleaner, humbug boiler, nightclub bouncer, Butlins breakfast cook and a gravedigger.